ECDL® Advanced

Revision Series

Advanced Database Software
Using Microsoft® Access®

Release RS14v2

Published by:

CiA Training Ltd
Business & Innovation Centre
Sunderland Enterprise Park
Sunderland SR5 2TA
United Kingdom

Tel: +44 (0) 191 549 5002
Fax: +44 (0) 191 549 9005

Email: info@ciatraining.co.uk
Web: www.ciatraining.co.uk

ISBN 13: 978-1-86005-808-0

First published 2009

European Computer Driving Licence, ECDL, International Computer Driving Licence, ICDL, and related logos are all registered Trade Marks of The European Computer Driving Licence Foundation Limited ("ECDL Foundation").

CiA Training Ltd is an entity independent of The British Computer Society using the name BCS, The Chartered Institute for IT ("BCS") and is not associated with ECDL Foundation or BCS in any manner.

BCS, The Chartered Institute for IT
APPROVED COURSEWARE

This courseware may be used to assist learners to prepare for the ECDL Certification Programme as titled on the courseware. Neither BCS nor **CiA Training Ltd** warrants that the use of this courseware publication will ensure passing of the tests for that ECDL Certification Programme.

This courseware publication has been independently reviewed and approved by BCS as covering the learning objectives for the ECDL Certification Programme.

Confirmation of this approval can be obtained by reviewing www.bcs.org/ecdl.

The material contained in this courseware publication has not been reviewed for technical accuracy and does not guarantee that candidates will pass the test for the ECDL Certification Programme.

Any and all assessment items and/or performance-based exercises contained in this courseware relate solely to this publication and do not constitute or imply certification by BCS or ECDL Foundation in respect of the ECDL Certification Programme or any other ECDL test.

Irrespective of how the material contained in this courseware is deployed, for example in a learning management system (LMS) or a customised interface, nothing should suggest to the candidate that this material constitutes certification or can lead to certification through any other process than official ECDL certification testing.

For details on sitting a test for an ECDL certification programme in the UK, please visit the BCS website at www.bcs.org/ecdl.

Learners using this courseware must be registered with BCS before undertaking a test for ECDL. Without a valid registration, the test(s) cannot be undertaken and no certificate, nor any other form of recognition, can be given to a learner. Registration should be undertaken with BCS at an Approved Centre.

CiA Training's **Revision Exercises** for **Advanced ECDL** contain a collection of revision exercises to provide support for students. They are designed to reinforce the understanding of the skills and techniques which have been developed whilst working through CiA Training's **Advanced ECDL** guides.

This training, which has been approved by BCS, The Chartered Institute for IT, includes exercise items intended to assist learners in their training for an ECDL Certification Programme. These exercises are not ECDL certification tests. For information about Approved Centres in the UK please visit the BCS website at www.bcs.org/ecdl.

Advanced Database Software - The revision exercises cover the following topics, grouped into sections:

- Database Fundamentals
- Creating Databases
- Using Lookup Fields
- Setting Field Properties
- Advanced Queries
- Creating Relationships
- Using Joins
- Creating Forms/Subforms
- Creating Form Controls
- Working with Reports
- Importing/Linking Data
- Creating Action Queries
- Using Query Wizards
- Macros

A minimum of two revision exercises are included for each section. There are also general exercises which cover techniques from any section of this guide. Answers are provided at the end of the guide wherever appropriate.

The Revision Exercises are suitable for:

- Any individual wishing to practise advanced features of this application. The user completes the exercises as required. Knowledge of *Access* is assumed, gained for example from working through the corresponding **ECDL Advanced** guide produced by **CiA Training**.

- Tutor led groups as reinforcement material. They can be used as and when necessary.

Downloading the Data Files

The data associated with these exercises must be downloaded from our website: ***www.ciatraining.co.uk/data_files***. Follow the on screen instructions to download the data files.

Your *FastCode* for this guide's data is: **RS14**

By default, the data files will be downloaded to the **CIA DATA FILES\Advanced ECDL Revision\AM5** folder in either **My Documents** or **Documents** depending in your version of ***Windows***.

The data required to complete the exercises is in the **Data** folder and worked solutions for every exercise can be found in the **Solutions** folder.

If you prefer, the data can be supplied on CD at an additional cost. Contact the Sales team at ***info@ciatraining.co.uk***.

Aims and Objectives

To provide the knowledge and techniques necessary to be able to successfully tackle the features of an advanced word processing application. After completing the exercises the user will have experience in the following areas:

- Creating databases
- Designing tables and setting field properties
- Performing advanced queries
- Creating and amending relationships
- Changing field properties
- Creating forms and form controls
- Creating reports and grouped reports
- Importing and linking data
- Creating action queries
- Creating and running macros

Office Versions

These revision exercises were written without references to any specific office version. The data is, however, Office specific and the correct set of data should be downloaded to match your office version.

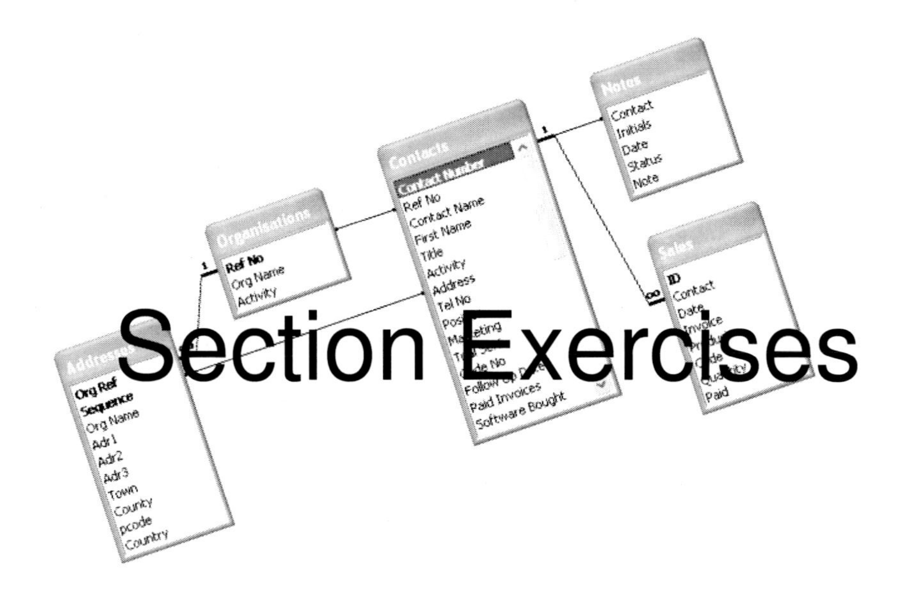

Section Exercises

The following revision exercises are divided into sections, each targeted at specific elements of the Advanced ECDL syllabus. The individual sections are an exact match for the sections in the ECDL Advanced Training Guides from CiA Training, making the guides an ideal reference source for anyone working through these exercises.

Fundamentals

These revision exercises include topics taken from the following list: database concepts, database development, SQL, creating a table, basic field properties.

Exercise 1

1. What does the term **SQL** stand for?

2. Are the following statements **True** or **False**?

    a) Access uses SQL to define queries.

    b) The SQL code behind a query can be displayed in Access.

    c) You need to know SQL in order to create queries.

    d) SQL is only used in Access applications.

3. Which two of the following are common types (models) of database?

    a) Hierarchical.

    b) SQL.

    c) Referential.

    d) Relational.

4. Arrange the following stages of database life cycle into a more realistic sequence:

    a) Data Entry.

    b) Database Creation.

    c) Database Design.

    d) Information Retrieval.

    e) Data Maintenance

5. A manufacturing company has a single integrated database system which holds data for many of its functions, including manufacturing, purchasing, accounting and personnel. Is this an example of a ?

   a) Website content management system.

   b) Enterprise resource planning system.

   c) Customer relationship management system.

   d) Dynamic website.

6. Which type of object must be present in an *Access* database: table, query or form?

Exercise 2

1. Which of the following database operations would require a technical knowledge of *Microsoft Access*?

   a) Add data to a table.

   b) Add a new field to a table.

   c) Change the columns in a report.

   d) Run a report.

2. Create a new database to log invoices for a scientific supplies company. Name the database **Invoices**.

3. Create the following table to be called **Details**. Select appropriate data types and field sizes for each field and add the first four records as shown below.

Invoice	Due	Customer Name	Customer Address	Item	Quantity	Price	Total Value
10012	05 January 2009	Conrads	27 High Street	Neutron Tubes	6	£1,500.00	£9,000.00
10016	06 January 2009	HiTek	Century Building	Spectrometer	1	£3,000.00	£3,000.00
10022	11 January 2009	Conrads	27 High Street	Power Packs	5	£75.00	£375.00
10029	12 January 2009	The Johnson Company	Johnson House	Power Packs	10	£75.00	£750.00

4. Give any reasons why this is not the most efficient design for a database.

5. Replace the **Customer Name** and **Customer Address** fields with a single **Customer Reference** field (length **6**). Use the following information to enter the customer information.

Customer Reference	Customer Name
C001	Conrads
H001	HiTek
J001	The Johnson Company

6. Remove the **Total Value** field from the table.

7. Change the format of the **Price** field to show **Euros**.

8. Change the format of the **Due** field to **Long Date**.

9. Adjust column widths so that all the headings and data are fully displayed.

10. Close the table, saving the design, then close the database.

Field Properties

These revision exercises include topics taken from the following list: creating lookup fields, changing formatting options, setting and modifying default values, setting mandatory fields, creating validation rules and text, creating input masks.

Exercise 3

1. Open the **Sarahs Salon** database. This has a table of **Bookings** and related tables for **Processes, Rooms** and **Technicians**. Look at the data in all the tables then open the **Bookings** table in **Design View**.

2. Change the **Field Properties** for **Date** so that it defaults to today's date (with no time component). The default value must change as the current date changes.

3. Create an input mask for the **Time** field based on the **Short Time** format. What is the resulting mask?

4. Create a validation rule for **Time** so that times greater than **17:30** will not be accepted. The validation text is to be **No bookings after 5:30 pm**.

5. Create a **Lookup** field for **Technician Name** that looks up the **Name** field from the **Technician** table. Restrict entries to those on the list.

6. Create an input mask for the **Room No** field so that only one character and one number will be accepted. The character will be converted automatically to upper case. What is the resulting mask?

7. Switch to **Datasheet View** and create a new record by typing in the following values (date should already be present as today's date):

Ref	Name	Date	Time	Process	Technician	Room	Comment
1409	**June Ball**	**'today'**	**1800**	**Pedicure**	**Bronwyn**	**aa22**	**Test**

8. You will be halted at the **Time** field (amend the entry to **1700**) and the **Technician** field (amend to **Lucy**). Confirm that because of the input masks, **1700** will appear as **17:00** and **aa22** will appear as **A2**.

9. Even though the field properties validations are all met, the new record still cannot be added. Why is this?

10. Change the **Process** to **Manicure** and add the record.

11. Add **Bronwyn** to the **Technician Name** table then amend the new booking record to show that name.

12. Close the database.

Exercise 4

1. Create a new database called **Booknow** to record telephone bookings for a theatre from registered customers.

2. Create a table called **Details** with the fields **Customer ID** (Text), **When** (Date/Time), **Performance** (Text), **Location** (Text), **No of Tickets** (Number). Do not define a primary key.

3. **Customer ID** values are always two upper case characters followed by 3 digits, e.g. **AB123**. Define an input mask to ensure that this format is always applied.

4. The **Performance** field can only be **Matinee**, **Early** or **Late**. Define a validation rule so that only one of these values can be entered.

5. The **Location** field can only be **Front Stalls**, **Rear Stalls**, or **Circle**. Define this field as a **Lookup** field (from a typed list) so that only one of these values can be selected.

6. What are the advantages of using a **Lookup** field rather than a **Validation Rule** to restrict entries to a limited set of values?

7. Add **Upper Circle** to the list of acceptable locations.

8. No more than three tickets can be booked on any one **Customer ID**. Set the maximum acceptable **No of Tickets** to **3** and define a suitable message to be displayed if the condition is not met.

9. A booking cannot be made unless all fields are completed. Make every field in the table mandatory.

10. Close the table, saving any changes if prompted and close the database.

Queries

These revision exercises include topics taken from the following list: using wildcards in queries, creating summary queries showing sum, count, average, maximum and minimum values, creating calculated fields using arithmetic operations, creating two variable parameter queries.

Exercise 5

1. Open the database **Periodic** showing details of some of the elements as classified in the Periodic table. Open the **Elements** table and examine the data.

2. Create and save a query called **Query1** to list the **Atomic Number**, **Name** and **Symbol**. Use a single wildcard criteria to select only elements whose symbol is the letter "c" followed by any vowel. What is the wildcard criteria and how many elements are selected?

3. Create and save a query called **Query2** to list the **Atomic Number**, **Name**, **Symbol** and **Boiling Point** for all elements whose boiling point is between **0°C** and **100°C**. How many are there?

4. The temperatures in the table are shown in degrees centigrade. It is also possible to show temperatures as degrees above absolute zero, or degrees absolute (sometimes called degrees Kelvin), where absolute zero is minus 273 degrees centigrade. Create a query to list the **Atomic Number**, **Name**, and **Symbol** for all elements classified as gases. Do not display the **Classification** field. Add a calculated field **Absolute**, which is defined as the **Boiling Point + 273**. How many degrees above absolute zero does liquid helium boil? Save the query as **Query4**.

5. Create a query called **Query5** to group the elements by **Classification** and show a count of the element names under each classification heading. How many are classified as liquids?

6. On the same query, add columns to show the average melting point and average boiling point for each classification.

7. In **Design View**, amend the field properties for the two average columns so that the data is displayed with a format of **Fixed**.

8. Create and save a query called **Query6** to list the **Atomic Number**, **Name** and **Symbol** for all elements not classified as metal. How many are there?

9. Make sure all queries are saved then close the database.

Exercise 6

1. Open the database **Commercial** showing details of some commercial premises for sale. Open the **Premises** table and examine the data.

2. Create and save a query called **Analysis1** to group the data by **Type of Premises** and show the average premises price in each category. Make sure the average price field is formatted as **Currency**. What type of premises has the lowest average price?

3. Create and save a query called **Analysis2** to group the data by **Location** and show the average price, the maximum price and the minimum price for each area. Make sure all fields are formatted as **Currency**.

4. Sort the query so that the location with the highest average price is shown first. Which location has the lowest average price?

5. Create and save a query called **Query1** to list the **Premises ID**, **Location**, **Address** and **Type of Premises**.

6. Add a calculated field called **Rate** to show the price per unit area for each premises. Format the new field as currency.

7. Change the query so that only premises with a rate value less than **500** and that are not **Manufacturing Units** are displayed. How many are there?

8. Save the query but leave it open.

9. Remove the **Type of Premises** selection criteria and replace the calculated field with the **Price** field.

10. Sort the data in ascending order of **Price** and use a setting on the toolbar/ribbon to display only the top three records in the sort order. Save the query as **Query2** and leave it open.

11. Remove the 'top three' selection and include a selection criteria so that the query will prompt for a **Type of Premises** value and an upper limit for **Price**, and only display the relevant records. Enter the text for the first prompt as **Which type?** and the second as **Up to Price?**

12. Run the query for **Store Unit** premises, up to **£80,000**. How many records are selected?

13. Save the query as **Query3** then close it and close the database.

Relationships

These revision exercises include topics taken from the following list: applying primary keys, applying and modifying different types of relationship (one to one, one to many, many to many, understanding joins (inner, outer, subtract, self), applying referential integrity and cascade options.

Exercise 7

1. Open the **Golf** database showing a table of senior members and their playing partners for a forthcoming pairs competition.

2. Create a query which will list all fields from the **Pairings** table, but also show the **Handicap** for the second person in the pairing. This will need a self join in the query, from the **Pairings** table to a copy of it.

3. Save the query as **Query1** and close the database.

4. Open the database **Salon** showing part of the advanced bookings data for a beauty salon. There are tables for **Bookings**, **Processes** and **Rooms**, but no relationships between them.

5. Apply primary keys to the first fields in the **Processes** and **Rooms** tables so that they can be used in **One to Many** relationships with the **Bookings** table.

6. Create **One to Many** relationships from both the **Processes** and **Rooms** to the **Bookings** table. Apply **Referential Integrity** to both relationships and select all cascade options.

7. Print out the relationships diagram.

8. Create a query showing **Booking Ref**, **Customer Name** and **Date** from the **Bookings** table with **Description**, **Duration** and **Charge** from the **Processes** table. Save the query as **Billing**.

9. View the **Rooms** table in **Datasheet View** and expand the subdatasheets to find which room is double booked (bookings on the same time and date). What are the details of the double booking?

10. Create a summary query based on the **Rooms** and **Bookings** tables, which counts the number of bookings, for each **Room Number**. Save the query as **Usage**. Why is there no record for room **A4**?

11. Change the join type for the **Rooms - Booking** link so that data for all rooms, including those with no usage, is shown in the query. What is the new type of join called?

12. Save the query and close the database.

Exercise 8

1. Open the database **Letting** showing part of the booking register for some holiday apartments. There are tables for **Units,** describing each apartment, and **Bookings**, listing the details of bookings for the apartments. There are no relationships between them.

2. Attempt to create a link with **Referential Integrity** between **Units** and **Bookings** based on the **Apartment** field. Why is this not allowed?

3. Cancel the relationship process without saving. Correct the problem by changing the design of the **Bookings** table, then create the link as described above. Do not select the cascade options.

4. Create a summary query to shows the total number nights from the **Booking** table for each **Apartment** on the **Units** table. Save the query as **Totals**.

5. Change the query to list only apartments that have no bookings. This will involve changing the **Join Type** to a **Subtract** join by using a selection. Save the amended query as **None**.

6. Apartment **35** is no longer available due to storm damage. Open the **Units** table and attempt to delete the record for apartment **35**. What is the outcome?

7. Edit the relationship between the tables so the cascade options are selected. Try to delete the record for **apartment 35** again. What is the outcome now?

8. Complete the deletion of the record and close the database.

Forms

These revision exercises include topics taken from the following list: creating main forms and sub forms, using subform wizard, linking forms.

Exercise 9

1. Open the **Sunny Holidays** database.

2. Use a wizard to create a form based on the **Units** table with a subform based on the **Bookings** table. Name the forms **Units2** and **Bookings2**. **Units2** should contain the fields **Unit**, **Location**, **Type**, **Beds** and **Weekly Charge**. **Bookings2** should contain the fields **Start Date**, **Nights** and **Name**. Specify a **Tabular** layout and a style of your choice.

3. When the form has been created add a new control to the right of **Weekly Charge** which calculates **5%** of the **Weekly Charge** value. Format the control as **Currency** and add a caption of **Early Payment Discount**.

4. Switch to **Form View** and add a new **Booking** in the subform for unit **S17** using your name.

5. Print a copy of the form showing this record.

6. Switch to **Design View** and delete the whole subform.

7. Make sure **Control Wizards** feature is switched on and use a button to add a new subform in the same position as before. The subform is to be based on the **Bookings** table and include the fields **Start Date**, **Nights** and **Name**. Show bookings for each unit, and call the subform **Bookings3**.

8. Use the new form to locate the record added in step 4.

9. Print a copy of the form showing this record then delete the record.

10. Close the form and close the database.

Exercise 10

1. Open the database **Sarahs Salon** and create a new query in **Design View**, based on the **Processes** and **Bookings** tables.

2. Add the following fields to the query grid in the order shown:

   The **Description** field from the **Processes** table.

   Booking Ref, **Customer Name**, **Date**, **Time** and **Room No** from the **Bookings** table.

   Save the query as **Details**.

3. Use a wizard to create a form and subform based on every field from the **Details** query. The data should be viewed by **Processes**. Specify a **Datasheet** layout and any style. Name the form **Booking Details**, and name the subform **Booking Subform**.

4. Use a wizard to create a form based on the **Bookings** table including the fields **Booking Ref**, **Customer Name**, **Date**, **Time** and **Room No**. Specify a **Datasheet** layout and any style. Give the form a title of **Manual Subform**.

5. Create a form in **Design View** including all the fields from the **Processes** table.

6. Without using the wizard, insert a subform based on the **Manual Subform** form below the existing fields. Use **Process** as the field to link the main form to the subform and give the form a title of **Manual Details**.

7. Enlarge the size of the subform if necessary to display all fields fully.

8. Locate the record for **Manicure** in the **Manual Details** form. How many bookings exist for this process?

9. Close the forms and the database.

Form Controls

These revision exercises include topics taken from the following list: using bound controls on forms (such as text boxes, combo boxes, list boxes, check boxes, option groups), using calculated fields on forms, modifying tab order, adding headers and footers.

Exercise 11

1. Open the database **Wages** and open the form **Pay**.

2. Delete the **Name** control from the form and replace it with a **Combo Box** with the same label.

3. The box is to look up values from the **Surname** field in the **Staff** table and store the results in the **Name** field of the **Pay** table.

4. Limit the possible values to those on the list.

5. Replace the **Department** control on the form with a **Combo Box** which will select from a typed list of **Production**, **Testing**, **Despatch**.

6. Store the result in the **Department** field.

7. Replace the **Rate** control on the form with a **List Box** containing the values **7.50**, **8.50**, **9.00**.

8. Store the result in the **Rate** field.

9. Replace the **Bonus** control on the form with an **Option Group** containing the **Label Names None**, **£50**, **£100** and the corresponding values **0**, **50**, **100**. The default selection is to be **None**.

10. Store the result in the **Bonus** field and specify **Sunken** style with a caption of **Bonus**.

11. Add a calculated field to the form, to the right of the **Bonus** option group. The calculation is to be **(Rate * Hours) + Bonus**, with a label of **Total Pay**.

12. Format the new calculated field as currency.

13. Change the tab order for the controls on the form so that they will be tabbed through in the same order as they appear on the form.

14. Save the form and check its operation by entering a few sample records.

15. Close the form and the database.

Exercise 12

1. Open the **Commercial** database.

2. Create a new form in design view based on the **Premises** table.

3. Place the fields **Premises ID**, **Location** and **Address**, **Type of Premises**, **Price**, **Unit Area** and **Floors** on the form. Make sure all fields are aligned.

4. Replace the current **Premises ID** control with a **Combo Box** with the same label.

5. The combo box is to show a list of the available **Premises ID** fields from the **Premises** table. The selected value from this field will be used to retrieve the relevant record to be displayed in the form.

6. Replace the current **Location** control with a **Combo Box** with the same label.

7. The combo box is to show a list of the existing **Location** fields from the **Premises** table, but each distinct location is only to appear once. Store the selected value from this field in the **Location** field.

8. Add a calculated field to the form, below the **Floors** field. The calculation is to be **(Price / Unit Area)**, with a label of **Price/Area**. Format the field as **Currency**.

9. Change the tab order for the controls on the form so that they will be tabbed through in the same order as they appear on the form.

10. Make sure form headers and footers are displayed and add a title **Main Premises Enquiry Form** to the header.

11. Format the title as **12pt**, **Bold**.

12. Save the form as **Enquiry** and close it.

13. Close the database.

Reports

These revision exercises include topics taken from the following list: creating grouped reports with totals, inserting page breaks, creating calculated fields in reports, inserting data fields in headers and footers, create subreports.

Exercise 13

1. Open the **Wages** database and open the **Staff Listing** report.
2. Change the report in **Design View** so that it is grouped by **Department**. Make sure that **Group Header** and **Group Footer** lines are shown.
3. Move the **Department** control from the **Detail** area to the same horizontal position in the **Department Header** area.
4. Change the properties so that each new department is shown on a new page, with the department name on the same page as the records.
5. The **Rate** field shows the hourly rate for each employee. Add a new calculated field to the right of **Rate** which calculates the basic weekly wage for a 37 hour week.
6. Remove the label from the calculated field and add an appropriately formatted entry of **Basic Week** to the headings in the **Page Header** area.
7. Format the calculated field as **Currency**.
8. In the **Department Footer** area show the average value of **Basic Week** for each department with a label of **Department Average**. Format the field as **Currency**.
9. Make sure the **Report Footer** area is shown and copy the **Department Average** controls into it. Change the label to **Company Average**.
10. What is the average basic weekly wage for the company?
11. Save and close the report and close the database.

Exercise 14

1. Use the **Commercial** database.
2. Use the wizard to create a grouped report based on the **Premises** table using the definitions in the following five steps.
3. Include the fields **Premises ID**, **Location**, **Address**, **Type of Premises**, **Price** and **Unit Area**.
4. Group the report by **Location** and sort in ascending order of **Price**.
5. Specify that the total and average price for each location is shown, as well as the price for each individual property.
6. Specify that the report will show the total price for each location as a percentage of the total price for all premises. Label this field **Percentage** and format it appropriately.
7. Specify **Landscape** layout and any style. Name the report **Report1**.
8. When the report has been generated, change the properties so that the premises for each location are shown on separate pages.
9. Format <u>all</u> summary price fields (not the percentage values) as **Currency**.
10. Include your name in the centre of the page footer area.
11. Print the report. Ensure that all field headings and data are fully displayed.
12. Close the database.

Import and Link Data

These revision exercises include topics taken from the following list: importing data in various formats, exporting data in various formats, linking a database to external data.

Exercise 15

1. Open the **Sunny Holidays** database. Extra information on apartment locations is available in the text file **Sites.csv** included with the supplied data files.

2. Import this file, creating a new table called **Sites** in the database. The first row contains column headings and the fields are delimited by commas. Choose the **Location** field to be the primary key.

3. Open the new table and adjust the column widths so that all data is fully displayed.

4. As a comparison, create another new table, this time by linking to the text file **Sites.csv**. Column headings and field delimiters are as before. Name the new table **Sites2**.

5. In the list of database tables, how can you tell that **Sites2** is linked? What restrictions does this place on the table?

6. Start *Word* and open the file **Sites.csv** (the file could also be opened in Excel if preferred).

7. Highlight the last record and delete it. Save and close the file, and close *Word.*

8. In the **Sunny Holidays** database, open the tables **Sites** and **Sites2** in **Datasheet View**. What is the difference between the tables?

9. Close the tables and the database.

Exercise 16

1. Create a new blank database named **Stores**.
2. Create a **Customers** table in the database by importing the **Customers** spreadsheet file from the supplied data folder.
3. The first row contains column headings. Choose the **Company** field to be the primary key.
4. Open the new table and make sure that all data is fully displayed.
5. Create a linked table called **Orders** in the database by linking to the **Orders** spreadsheet file from the supplied data folder. The first row contains column headings.
6. Open the new table and make sure that all data is fully displayed.
7. Create a relationship between the **Customers** table and the **Orders** table using the **Company** and **Customer** fields respectively.
8. Create a query containing the fields **Order, Date**, **Value** and **Paid** from the **Orders** table, **Company** and **Contact** from **Customers**.
9. Restrict the query to orders that have not been paid (Paid = Null) and save it as **Not Paid**.
10. Run the query. How many records are included?
11. Close the query and open the **Orders** spreadsheet in *Excel.*
12. Add today's date to the **Paid** column for order **001**. Save the spreadsheet.
13. In *Access*, run the **Not Paid** query again. How many records are selected now?
14. Close the database.
15. Close the **Orders** spreadsheet and close *Excel.*

Action Queries

These revision exercises include topics taken from the following list: creating append queries, creating delete queries, making a table from a query, creating an update query. If any action queries do not run, check the security options for your *Access* installation.

Exercise 17

1. Open the database **Commercial**.
2. It is decided to produce a separate table containing details of premises that have not had offers. Create a query which will create a new table in the database.
3. The new table is to be called **Sale** and will contain the fields **Premises ID**, **Location**, **Address, Type of Premises** and **Price** from the **Premises** table. Only records from the **Premises** table with an **Offers** value of **0** (zero) are to be included.
4. Run the query then save it as **Sale Create**. How many records are in the new table?
5. Create another query which will reduce the **Price** of all records in the **Sale** table by **20%**.
6. Run the query and save it as **Sale Update**.
7. It is decided that manufacturing units should not be included in the sale. Create a query which deletes any record from the **Sale** table where the **Type of Premises** is **Manufacturing Unit**.
8. Run the query and save it as **Sale Remove**. How many records are now in the **Sale** table?

9. Create a query to add a single record from the **Premises** table to the **Sale** table. All necessary fields are to be added (see step 3). The record is to be selected by means of a prompt for the **Premises ID** value. Make the prompt text **Add which record**.

10. Save the query as **Sale Add**.

11. Run the **Sale Add** query and specify premises **M002** to be added. Check the **Sale** table to make sure the record for **M002** is added, and check the **Premises** table to make sure the record has not been removed.

12. Close the **Commercial** database.

Exercise 18

1. Open the database **Orders**. The **Outstanding** table shows the outstanding orders for four products that are to be despatched from three warehouses within a company.

2. A system is required to move batches of orders from the **Outstanding** table to the **Despatched** table.

3. Create a query which will place a '**D**' in the **Despatch** field and today's date in the **Date** field, of every record in the **Outstanding** table for the **Main** warehouse.

4. Run the query and save it as **Order Update**.

5. Create a query which will take every record from the **Outstanding** table with a '**D**' in the **Despatch** field and append it to the **Despatched** table. Make sure all three fields which make up a record in the **Despatched** table are completed.

6. Run the query and save it as **Order Append**.

7. Create a query which will delete every record from the **Outstanding** table with a '**D**' in the **Despatch** field.

8. Run the query and save it as **Order Delete**.

9. How many records are there now in the **Outstanding** and **Despatched** tables?

10. Close the **Orders** database.

Query Wizards

These revision exercises include topics taken from the following list: creating a crosstab query, creating a find duplicates query, creating a find unmatched query.

Exercise 19

1. Open the **Sarahs Salon** database.

2. Use **Find Duplicates Query Wizard** to create a query to check if any rooms are double booked, i.e. if there are any records with the same room, date and time.

3. Run the query and save it as **Double Booked**.

4. Which room, if any, is involved in double booking?

5. Use the **Find Unmatched Query Wizard** to create a query to find if any rooms are not used in any current booking. Save the query as **Unused**.

6. Run the query. Which room, if any, is not involved in any booking?

7. Close the database.

8. Open the **Letting** database.

9. Create a **Crosstab** query which will show the total number of nights booked in a grid of Apartment (rows) and Week Number (columns). Make sure the query includes a summary value for each apartment and name the query **Booking Grid**.

10. Run the query. How many nights are booked for apartment 20 during this period?

11. Open the query in **Design View** and change the **Total of Nights** heading to **Nights Booked**.

12. Save the changes to the query and close it.

13. Close the database.

Exercise 20

1. Open the **Deliveries** database. The **Despatched** table lists deliveries made for four different products from three warehouses for the first three months of the year.

2. Create a query based on the **Despatched** table which will show on a grid the total number of deliveries of each item for each warehouse in the following format:

	Warehouse	Warehouse
Item		
Item		

3. Save the query as **Item Deliveries by Warehouse**. How many deliveries of Sprangs were made from the Newtown warehouse in this period?

4. Create a query with the same format showing the total quantity of each item delivered from each warehouse.

5. Save the query as **Item Quantity by Warehouse**. How many Sprangs were delivered from the Newtown warehouse in this period?

6. Create a similar query showing the total quantity of each item delivered each month.

7. Save the query as **Item Quantity by Month**. Which month saw the greatest number of **Assemblies** delivered?

8. Close the database.

Macros

These revision exercises include topics taken from the following list: understanding macro actions, creating a macro, attaching a macro to a control, creating macros from controls.

Exercise 21

1. Open the **Wages** database.

2. Create a new macro in the database to open the **Staff** table in **Datasheet** view and then maximise it. Ensure that no changes can be made to the **Staff** table.

3. Save the macro as **Staffview**.

4. Create another macro containing two actions, one to close the **Weekly** form and one to quit *Access*. Save the macro as **Shut Down**.

5. Open the **Weekly** form in design view.

6. Add a **Command Button** control in the **Form Header** area, right of the title.

7. Use any method to attach the **Staffview** macro to the control so that it is activated when the button is clicked.

8. Add the caption **Staff List** to the button.

9. With the wizard switched off, add a **Command Button** control to the right of the **Staff List** button.

10. Change the properties of the new **Command Button** control so that the **Shut Down** macro is activated only when the button is double clicked.

11. Add the caption **Quit** to the button.

12. Open the **Weekly** form. Click the **Staff List** button to check that the staff list is displayed, then close the **Staff** table.

13. Double click the **Quit** button to close the form and quit *Access*. Start *Access* again if you are continuing with further exercises.

Exercise 22

1. Open the **Commercial** database.

2. Create a macro which will close the current form and open the **Price List** report in **Print Preview** mode. Save the macro as **Prices**.

3. Open the form **Start** in **Design View** and display the properties for **Price** field.

4. Define an **Event** for the field so that when it is doubled clicked, the **Prices** macro is run.

5. Leave the form open and view the **Offer** macro in **Design View**.

6. This macro will set the value of the **Offer Date** field to today's date. Close the macro and on the **Start** form, change the properties of the **Offers** control so that whenever the value is updated (**After Update Event**) the **Offer** macro is run.

7. Save the form and switch to **Form View**. Double click the **Price** control to confirm that the form closes and the **Price List** report is shown.

8. Close the report and open the **Start** form in **Form View** again.

9. Change or add an **Offers** value and press <**Enter**>. Check that the correct date is entered into the **Offer Date** field.

10. Close the form and the database.

General Exercises

The following revision exercises can involve processes from any part of the ECDL advanced syllabus.

Exercise 23

1. Open the **Time Sheet** database. This is a system to allocate the time spent by employees on various projects. Open the **Staff** table and change the **Department** field size to **20**.

2. Change the **Department** field to a **Lookup** field that will only accept values from the following typed list: **Technical**, **Training**, **Marketing**, **Administration**. Save and close the table.

3. The time sheet data is held in a spreadsheet called **Weeks**. Import this data as a new table, **Time Sheet**. The first row of the spreadsheet contains column headings. Do not define any primary keys.

4. Open the **Time Sheet** table. Set the field size of the text fields to **20** and make sure none of the fields are indexed. Change the **Days Worked** field to have a field size of **Single** and a **Fixed** format with **1** decimal place.

5. Create a validation rule for the **Week No** field so that only numbers in the range 1 – 52 can be entered. Create a text message **Only Week Numbers 1 – 52 to be used**, which will display if the validation conditions are not met. Save and close the table.

6. Create a relationship between the **Time Sheet** table and the **Staff** table based on **Staff No**, and between the **Time Sheet** table and the **Project** table based on **Project Code**. Specify referential integrity for both joins and apply all cascade options.

7. Create a query based on the **Project**, **Staff** and **Time Sheet** tables. Include **Project Code**, **Project Name**, **Staff No**, **Surname**, **Department**, **Week No** and **Days Worked**. Save the query as **Query1**.

8. In **Query1**, use wildcards to select only records where **1** is the middle digit of the **Staff No**. Save the query as **Query2**.

9. Remove the selection from **Query2**, and add selections for project code and department which can be specified each time the query is run. Add the text **Which Project?** as the project code prompt message, and **Which Department?** as the department prompt message. Save the query as **Query3**.

10. Run **Query3** to find how many people have been off sick (project code **Sick**) in the **Training** department over the four week period.

11. Create a summary query based on the **Project** and **Time Sheet** tables which shows the **Project Code**, **Project Name** and the total **Days Worked** on each project. Save the query as **Query4** and run it. What is the total number of days spent on the **Daley Cars** project?

12. Change the criteria in **Query4** to show only the projects that have had no time spent on them. The properties of the join between **Project** and **Time Sheet** tables in the query will need to be amended for the query to work. Save the query as **Query5**. Which two projects are selected?

13. Use the wizard to create a report based on the query **Query1**. Include the fields **Project Name**, **Week No**, **Surname**, and **Days Worked**. View the data by **Project** and sort the records by **Surname** within each group.

14. Specify summary options which will show the total value of **Days Worked** and also include detail records.

15. Select **Portrait** orientation and any style. Name the report **Project Analysis**.

16. Make sure that the records for each **Project Name** start on a new page. How many pages are there in the report? Print the pages for the first project only.

17. Open the form **Project List** and add a command button on the right of the form header area. Without using a macro, specify an action that will print out the **Project Analysis** report when the button is clicked. Add a caption of **Analysis** to the button. Save the form.

18. Create a crosstab query based on the **Query1** query with row headings of **Surname**, and column headings of **Project Code**. The calculated data is the sum of **Days Worked**. Save the query as **Crosstab1**.

19. Close the database.

Exercise 24

1. Open the **Repairs** database. This contains a table listing records of computers and another table listing records of repairs to those computers. What is the main database design reason for not having all the information in one table?

2. Create a relationship between the **Computers** and **Repairs** tables based on the **Serial Number** fields in each table. Try to specify Referential Integrity. What is the error message which prevents you?

3. Create the relationship without Referential Integrity then open the **Computers** table in **Design View**. Define the **Serial Number** field as a **Primary Key** and save the changes.

4. Edit the relationship between the tables and apply referential integrity. What type of relationship is created?

5. Open the **Computers** table and add a new field called **Telephone**, immediately after the **Town** field. Set the data type to **Text** and the field size to **15**. Make the field mandatory.

6. Define an input mask for the new field so that the first character is a zero, followed by three mandatory numeric characters, followed by a dash, followed by seven mandatory numeric characters.

7. Save the changes and enter a dummy telephone number for the first record on the **Computers** table so that it is accepted by the input mask.

8. Open the **Repairs** table and change the **Engineer** field to a Lookup field which will select an entry from the typed list: **Keith**, **John**, **Stephen**, **David**, **Richard**, **Albert**. Set the field properties so that only values from the list are allowed.

9. Create a query which shows **Title**, **First Name** and **Owner** from the **Computers** table and **Job Description**, **Price** and **Date** from the **Repairs** table. Sort the records in descending **Price** order and run the query to show only the top 5 priced jobs. Save the query as **Top Price**.

10. Display the query so that the SQL code is seen. Copy the lines of code and paste them into an empty document in *Word* (or *Wordpad* or *Notepad*). Print out the lines of code and close *Word* without saving.

11. Create and run a query which will make a new table called **Overdue** (in 2007/2010/2013, make sure content is enabled). The new table is to contain the same the fields as the previous query, but only those records dated before **15/05/2004**. Save the query as **New**.

12. Create and run a query which will update the **Price** field for all records in the **Overdue** table to a value **10%** higher (Price*1.1). Save the query as **Extra**.

13. Create and run a query which shows a single summary record for each engineer with the total price of all their jobs. What is the total value of all David's jobs? Save the query as **Summary**.

14. Open the **Computer Records** form and add the newly created **Telephone** field to the right of **Town**.

15. Use a button on the **Toolbox** to add a subform to the lower part of the form, based on the existing form **Repair Records**. Make the subform about 15cm wide by 3cm high. Save the **Computer Records** form.

16. Open the **Computer Main** report and delete the existing linked subreport.

17. Create a new linked subreport in the same position as the old one, based on the **Repair Detail** report. Use the default **Serial Number** field as the link.

18. Save the new version of the **Computer Main** report.

19. Close the database.

Exercise 25

1. Open the **Agents** database. This contains a table of commercial premises available for sale.

2. Open the **Premises** table and change the data type of the fields **Occupied**, **Lift** and **Disabled Access** to **Yes/No**. Make sure that the control is set to display each field as a **Check Box**.

3. Create and run a query which shows the distribution of types of premises by location, displayed in a grid form with **Type of Premises** as the columns and **Location** as the rows. The data in the grid should be the number of premises.

4. Save the query as **Grid** and run it. Only two types of premises are available in **Dockland**, what are they?

5. A list of offers received for the premises exists on a spreadsheet called **Offers**. Import this file so as to create a new embedded table called **Offers** in the database. No primary key is required. Save and close the table.

6. Create another table, called **Offers2**, which is linked to the **Offers** spreadsheet. Save and close the table and close the database.

7. Open the **Offers** spreadsheet in *Excel*, change the value of the first offer, save the file and close *Excel*. Open the **Agents** database. Which table contains the revised offer value: **Offers**, **Offers2** or both of them?

8. Open the **Offers** table in **Design View**. The format of the **Client Code** field must be a single upper case character followed by 2 digits. Add an input mask to the field properties to ensure that this format is always used.

9. If properties have more than one offer, only the highest one is to be considered. Create and run query called **Duplicates** which lists duplicate occurrences of **Premises ID** in the **Offers** table. Show all fields from the table. Which two properties are listed?

10. For each property listed, delete the lower value offer (2 records). Close the query and run it again. There should now be no records selected.

11. Create and run a query called **No Offers** which lists all fields for all records on the **Premises** table that do not have a matching record (with the same **Premises ID**) on the **Offers** table. How many records are selected?

12. Create a relationship between the **Premises** and **Offers** tables based on the **Premises ID** field. Specify Referential Integrity and apply all cascade options.

13. Create and run a query based on both tables. Show the **Premises ID, Location, Address,** and **Price** from **Premises**, and **Offer Price** from **Offers**. How many records are displayed? Save the query as **Check**.

14. Open the report **Offers List**. This is a report based on the **Check** query, sorted by **Location**, and will only run correctly if the **Check** query was successfully created in step **13**.

15. Insert a new control at the right of the **Detail** area, which calculates **Offer Price** as a fraction of **Price**. Format the control as **Percent** and delete the caption. Add a caption of **Percent** in the appropriate place in the **Page Header** area.

16. The report is already sorted by **Location**, change the properties so that change of location also displays a group header but no group footer.

17. Move the **Location** field from the **Detail** area directly upwards into the **Location Header** area and reduce the height of the **Location Header** area to **1cm**.

18. Change the properties of the **Location Header** area so that the records for each location begin on a new page.

19. Add the date to the left side of the **Page Footer** area so that it will always show the current date. Add your name to the middle of the **Page Footer** area and print out page 3 only of the report. Close the database.

Exercise 26

1. Open the **Expenses** database which contains tables for employees (**Staff**), current projects (**Project**), and expense details (**Data**) for a software development company. Make the first fields in the **Staff** and **Project** tables into the **Primary Keys**.

2. Create a query to build a new table called **Claims**, which only includes records from the **Data** table that have dates between the **1st Jan 2004** and **30th June 2004** inclusive. Include all fields.

3. Save the query as **Build** and run it. How many records are included in the new table?

4. Open the **Claims** table and change the data type for the **Project Code** field so that values can only be entered by selecting them from a look up list of existing **Project Code** fields from the **Project** table. Make sure that only values from the list will be accepted.

5. Create relationships between **Staff** and **Claims** using the **Staff No** field, and between **Project** and **Claims** using the **Project Code** field. Apply referential integrity and all cascade options.

6. Create a query which will include fields from the **Staff**, **Project** and **Claims** tables in the following order, with the records sorted alphabetically by **Surname**.

    Surname, **First Name** (from **Staff**), **Project Name** (from **Project**), and **Date**, **Expense Type**, and **Amount** (from **Claims**).

7. Use criteria to restrict the query to claims made on or after **1st April 2004**, which are also over **£1000**. Save the query as **Large** and run it. How many records are found?

8. Create a summary query based on the **Project** and **Claims** tables which will show one line for each different project. Show the **Project Name** on each line and save the query as **Project Summary**. How many records does the query produce? Why is this different to the number of records on the **Project** table.

9. On the **Project Summary** query, add columns to show the total number of claims, the total value of claim amounts, the maximum and minimum claim amounts, and the average claim amount, for each project. Save the query.

10. By applying various sorts, determine the projects with the highest average claim amount, the highest number of claims and the lowest total claim amount. Leave the query sorted in ascending order of total amount and save it.

11. Use a wizard to create a form showing all the fields from the **Staff** and **Claims** tables. View the data by Staff as a form with subform. Choose a **Datasheet** layout and any style. Accept the names **Staff** and **Claims Subform** for the names of the forms.

12. Hide the **Staff No** column in the subform area by reducing the width to zero.

13. Change the width of the subform area and the width of the individual subform columns to improve the appearance of the form. Use whatever Views are most convenient.

14. Open the **NewStaff** form and replace the **Department** control with an option group. Include three option buttons with labels **Analysis**, **Support**, and **Training**, and values of **1**, **2** and **3** with no default value. The value is to be stored in the **Department** field. Define a caption of **Department** for the group.

15. Open the report **Staff Summary**. Add a new control to the right of **Amount** in the **Detail** area, to calculate a 5% increase to the amount value (multiply by 1.05). Format the control as currency and add a heading of **To Pay** in the **Page Header** area.

16. The report is already grouped by **Staff Number**. Display a group footer area for this grouping level.

17. Add controls to the appropriate part of the group footer area to display totals for both the **Amount** and **To Pay** figures. Format these as currency.

18. Add the current date and time as a field to the right of the **Report Header**, and the page number in the format **Page x of y** to the left of the **Page Footer**.

19. Save the report and print the first 2 pages, then close the database.

Exercise 27

1. Open the **Sports** database. This contains a table of Sports Centre members (**Members**) and available classes (**Classes**). A **Registration** table shows which members are enrolled in which classes.

2. Open the **Members** table. Format the **Membership Type** field so that it is a mandatory field and will only accept values looked up from the following typed list:

   AC, AM, JC, JM, SC, SM

3. Open the **Classes** table. Apply an input mask to the **Class Code** field so it must always consist of one upper case alphabetic character and one digit.

4. One member can be enrolled in several classes and each class can involve several members. What is the name of the additional component required to set up a many-to-many relationship between these tables. Create a many-to-many relationship between the **Members** and **Classes** table, making use of the **Registration** table. Apply referential integrity to all joins.

Note: *This relationship must be correctly defined before the rest of the exercise can be attempted. The correct solution is shown in the Answers section at the end of the exercises.*

5. Create a query showing **Class Code** and **Class** from the **Classes** table and **Last Name** from the **Members** table. Include any other tables that may be necessary. Sort the query by **Class Code** and restrict it to records with the text **gym** in the **Class** field. Save the query as **Query1** and run it. How many records are selected?

6. Create a query based on the **Classes** and **Registration** tables only, which will show only the total number of members enrolled in each **Class Code**. Sort the records in ascending order of number of members. Save the new query as **Query2**.

7. Change the properties of the join in **Query2** so that classes without members are also shown. Add selection criteria so that only classes without members are shown. Save the query and run it. Which classes have no members?

8. Create a query called **Addnew** which selects all records on the **New** table with the **Paid** field set to **Yes**, and adds them to the **Members** table. Save the query and run it. How many records are added?

9. Create a query called **Remove** which deletes those records from the **New** table that were added to the **Members** table in the previous step. Save the query and run it.

10. Create a query called **Newcost** which updates the **Classes** table by adding **£5** to the **Basic Cost** field for each class except the **Tennis** classes. Save the query and run it.

11. Open the **Payment** form. Change the tab order of the fields to be the same as their actual order on the form.

12. Add a control underneath **Basic Cost** to show any allowable discount for this record (basic cost multiplied by discount). Format the control as currency, and add a caption of **Less Discount**.

13. Add a control to the right of this which shows the amount to pay, after the discount has been subtracted. Format the control as before, and add a caption of **To Pay**.

14. Add a command button to the top right of the form. Define a caption of **Classes** and attach the **Open Classes** macro so that it will run when the button is clicked.

15. Add the current date (no time) as a field in the bottom left of the detail area, above the black line. Save the form and print the first page only.

16. Use the wizard to create a report based on **Query5** (this query includes all data from the **Members** and **Classes** tables). Select the fields **Class**, **Class Code**, **Day**, **Time**, **Membership No**, **Last Name** in that order. Group the report by **Class** and select **Landscape** orientation and any style. Save the report as **Timetable**.

17. Replace the **Last Name** field with a field that concatenates **Title**, **First Name**, and **Last Name**. Change the label in the page header to **Full Name**.

18. Change the properties of the report so that each **Class** group starts on a new page.

19. Close all open objects and close the database.

Exercise 28

1. Open the **Fells** database. This contains a table of Lakeland fells (**Mountain**) and some established routes to their summits (**Routes**). A third table (**Ascents**) logs details of some actual ascents using these routes.

2. View the relationship between the tables. Does it indicate:
    a) One mountain can have many routes
    b) One route can apply to many mountains
    c) Only one route is allowed per mountain
    d) All of the above.

3. Open the **Routes** table in **Datasheet** view and look at the **Links** column for the first two records. What features indicate that this is a functioning hyperlink?

4. Create and save a query called **Height** based on the **Mountain** table. Include all the fields. The query will select all records within a range of heights which will be entered each time the query runs.

    Enter a parameter in the **Metres** field to select records that are greater or equal to the entered value. Use a parameter prompt of **From**.

    Enter a second parameter to select records that are lower or equal to the entered value. Use a parameter prompt of **To**. The two criteria are to be connected using an **And** condition.

5. Run the query and enter **500** at the **From** prompt and **600** at the **To** prompt to list all fells between 500 and 600 metres high. How many are there?

6. Create and save a query called **NoGrades** displaying all fields from the **Routes** table. Display only routes which do not have grades. What is the criteria used in the query? What would the criteria have to be to display only routes that do have grades?

7. Create a query called **High** which displays the highest **20%** of fells from the **Mountains** table. Include all available fields from the table on the display.

8. Create a query called **Region** based on the **Mountain** table which displays the height of the highest fell for each Region. The fell name is not to be shown.

9. Open the form **Main** in **Design View**. This form is based on the **Routes** table. Is the header **Lakeland Fells** a bound or an unbound control? Why? Is the field **Route** a bound or an unbound control? Why?

10. Delete the control **Fell Name** and replace it with a combo box which will retrieve its values from a list of **Fell Names** from the **Mountain** table. The value is to be stored in the **Fell Name** field on the **Routes** table and the control is to have a label of **Fell**.

11. Change the **Tab Order** of the form so that the combo box is between the **Route** and the **Description** fields in the control sequence.

12. Add **Form2**, which displays records from the **Ascents** table, as a subform on the right side of the **Main** form. The **Ascents** and **Routes** tables are not linked so the link will have to be specified as the subform is added. The linking field from both tables is **Route**. Define the name for the subform as **Ascents**.

13. Open the **Log** report. Add a new column heading of **Height (ft)** at the right of the **Page Header** area. Add a calculated control in the **Detail** area which shows the mountain height in feet (assume **3.28** feet in a metre).

14. Total this calculated value in the appropriate places in the **Month Footer** and **Report Footer** areas. Format all the new controls as **Fixed** with no decimal places.

15. Change both totals in the **Month Footer** area to be running totals which will accumulate over the whole report. How many metres had been climbed by the end of March (month 3)?

16. Add your name to the right of the **Report Header**, then save the report and print it.

17. Open the report **Heights**. This displays all fells in descending height order. Add an extra column to the right of the **Metres** column showing the height as a percentage of the total height of all fells. Format as **Percentage**.

18. Add the current date to the left side of the **Page Footer** area, in the format **01 January 2005** with no time values.

19. Save the report and print it, then close the database.

This section contains answers to all specific questions posed in the preceding exercises, together with the name of the file or files containing the worked solution for each exercise.

Note: *If any features of the solutions appear not to run, check your computer security settings. It may often be necessary to select the **Enable this content** option from the **Security Warning** banner.*

Exercise 1

Step 1 Structured Query Language.

Step 2 **a**. True, **b**. True, **c**. False, **d**. False.

Step 3 **a** and **d**.

Step 4 **c** Database Design,

b Database Creation,

a Data Entry,

e Data Maintenance,

d Information Retrieval.

Step 5 **b**, Enterprise resource planning system.

Step 6 Every database must have at least one table.

A sample solution for this exercise can be found in the **Health Solution** database in the **Solutions** folder.

Exercise 2

Step 1 b) Adding a new field would definitely require technical knowledge to ensure that it was defined correctly and to assess the implications to other parts of the database.

c) Changing report columns would require some technical knowledge of report formatting.

Step 4 Customer name and address will be duplicated on every invoice record for the same company.

Value does not need to be held in the table, it can be calculated whenever it is needed.

An invoice can only contain one item.

A sample solution for this exercise can be found in the **Invoices Solution** database in the **Solutions** folder.

Exercise 3

Step 3 **00:00;0;**

Step 4 enter **<=17.30**, converted to **<=#17:30:00#**

Step 6 **>L0**

Step 9 Because this table is linked to the **Processes** table with referential integrity, and **Pedicure** does not exist as a process.

A sample solution for this exercise can be found in the **Sarahs Solution** database in the **Solutions** folder.

Exercise 4

Step 3 Input mask **>LL000**

Step 6 All possible values can be seen in advance in the lookup list, and no typing is involved, only selection

A sample solution for this exercise can be found in the **Booknow Solution** database in the **Solutions** folder.

Exercise 5

Step 2 Like **"C[aeiou]*"**
3 records.

Step 3 **1**

Step 4 **4** degrees

Step 5 **2** are liquids

Step 8 **18** are not metals

A sample solution for this exercise can be found in the **Periodic Solution** database in the **Solutions** folder.

Exercise 6

Step 2 Store Unit

Step 4 Industrial Park

Step 7 **17** premises

Step 11 **6** premises

A sample solution for this exercise can be found in the **Commercial Solution** database in the **Solutions** folder.

Exercise 7

Step 7

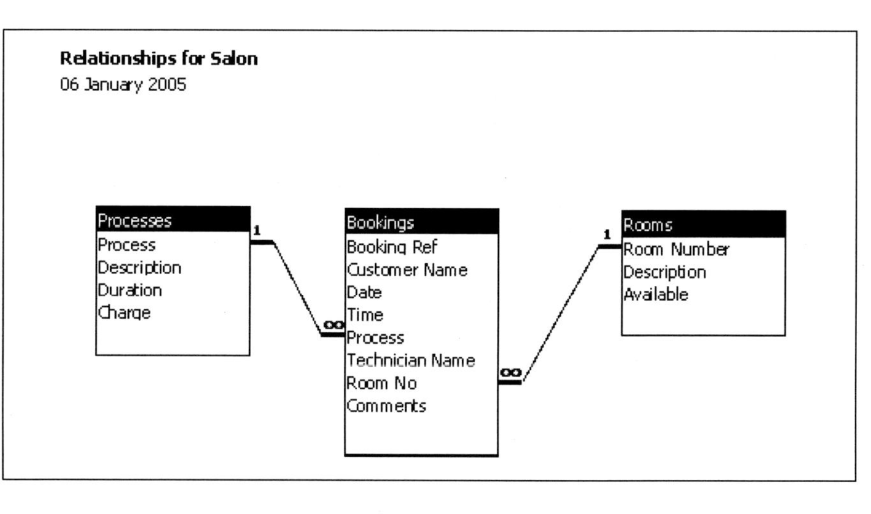

Step 9 Room **A2** has 2 bookings for 10:00

Step 10 Because the default join will only show records that have entries in **Rooms** and **Bookings**, and room **A4** has no bookings.

Step 11 **Outer Join**

Sample solutions for this exercise can be found in the **Golf Solution** and **Salon Solution** databases in the **Solutions** folder.

Exercise 8

Step 2 Because the **Apartment** field is defined as **Number** in the **Units** table, and **Text** in the **Bookings** table. They must be the exactly the same data type to define a link with referential integrity.

Step 6 If referential integrity is on and the cascade options are off, the record cannot be deleted because there are matching records on the **Bookings** table.

Step 7 If the cascade options are on, the record and all associated records from **Bookings** will be deleted after a warning.

A sample solution for this exercise can be found in the **Letting Solution** database in the **Solutions** folder.

Exercise 9

Step 5

Unit: S17
Location: San Marco
Type: Large 3 room
Beds: 6
Weekly Charge: £500.00 Early Payment Discount: £25.00
Bookings2

	Start Date	Nights	Name
	12/06/2004	14	Ms Ripley
▶	26/06/2004	7	Mr Barnacle
*			

Record: 2 of 2

A sample solution for this exercise can be found in the **Sunny Solution** database in the **Solutions** folder.

Exercise 10

Step 8 **4** records

A sample solution for this exercise can be found in the **Sarahs Solution** database in the **Solutions** folder.

Exercise 11

Weekly Pay Details

Employee: Branson
Department: Production
Date: 06/01/2005
Rate: 7.50 / 8.50 / 9.00
Hours Worked: 35
Bonus: None / £50 / £100
Total Pay: £347.50

A sample solution for this exercise can be found in the **Wages Solution** database in the **Solutions** folder.

Exercise 12

A sample solution for this exercise can be found in the **Commercial Solution** database in the **Solutions** folder. The final form should be similar to this after selecting the premises **M008**. Remember it may be necessary to '**Enable Content**' in *Access 2007/2010/2013* to allow the form to function.

Main Premises Enquiry Form

Premises ID	M008
Location	Riverside Complex
Address:	Suite A, The Marina
Type of Premises:	Conference Unit
Price:	£150,000.00
Unit Area:	300
Floors:	1
Price/Area	£500.00

Record: 8 of 40

Exercise 13

Step 10 **£374.35**

A sample solution for this exercise can be found in the **Wages Solution** database in the **Solutions** folder. The layout of the final page of the **Staff Listing** report should look similar to this.

Department	Staff No	Surname	First Name	Start Date	Rate	Basic Week
Testing						
	20	Parry	Nolene	13/01/2001	£9.00	£333.00
	18	Terry	Margaret	17/04/2003	£8.50	£314.50
	10	Bluebell	Neil	22/07/1998	£8.50	£314.50
				Department Average		£320.67
				Company Average		£374.35

Exercise 14

A sample solution for this exercise can be found in the **Commercial Solution** database in the **Solutions** folder. The layout of the first page of **Report1** should look similar to the following diagram.

Report1

Location	Price	Premises ID	Address	Type of Premises	Unit Area
Central Area					
	£56,000.00	P010	The Lothian Suites	Conference Unit	300
	£75,000.00	M002	10 Willow Road	Office Premises	60
	£100,000.00	M006	16 Station Road	Office Premises	200
	£100,000.00	M014	12th Floor, Stanton Tower	Office Premises	150
	£156,000.00	P012	17 Hartson Chambers	Office Premises	145
	£200,000.00	P001	15 Lothian Enterprise Buildin	Office Premises	600
	£250,000.00	M011	5th Floor, Stanton Tower	Office Premises	400
	£300,000.00	M012	Raby Exhibition Hall	Exhibition Hall	400

Summary for 'Location' = Central Area (8 detail records)

Sum	£1,237,000.00
Avg	£154,625.00
Standard	29.59%

Exercise 15

Step 5 The linked table has a different icon (the picture shown below is from *Access XP*). Design modifications are limited for the linked table.

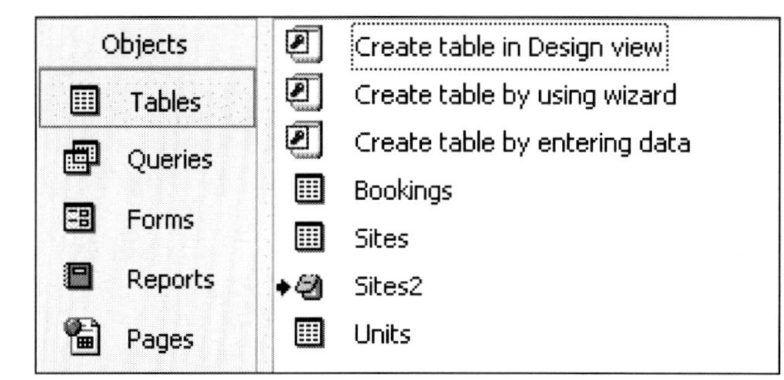

Step 8 **Sites** will remain as it was, **Sites2** will have a missing record.

A sample solution for this exercise can be found in **Sunny Solution.mdb** in the **Solutions** folder (because of path differences, the linked table in the solution may not open without using **Linked Table Manager** to locate it).

Exercise 16

Step 10 **20** records.

Step 13 **19** records

A sample solution for this exercise can be found in the **Stores Solution** database in the **Solutions** folder (because of path differences, the linked table in the solution may not open without using **Linked Table Manager**).

Exercise 17

Step 4 **10** records

Step 8 **7** records

A sample solution for this exercise can be found in the **Commercial Solution** database in the **Solutions** folder.

Exercise 18

Step 9 **13** records in Outstanding, **10** in Despatched

A sample solution for this exercise can be found in the **Orders Solution** database in the **Solutions** folder.

Exercise 19

Step 4 Room **A2** double booked on **14/04/2004**

Step 6 Room **A4** not involved in any bookings

Step 10 Apartment 20 has **49** nights booked during this period

Sample solutions for this exercise can be found in the **Sarahs Solution** database and **Lettings Solution.mdb** database in the **Solutions** folder.

Exercise 20

Step 3 There were **4** deliveries of **Sprangs** from **Newtown**.

Step 5 There were **800 Sprangs** delivered from **Newtown**.

Step 7 **March**

A sample solution to the steps in this exercise can be found in the **Deliveries Solution** database in the **Solutions** folder.

Exercise 21

Step 12

Weekly Pay Details   Staff List   Quit

Name   Dumalu

Department   Production

Date   06/01/2005

Rate   £8.50

Hours   35

Bonus   50

Record: 1 of 1

A sample solution for this exercise can be found in the **Wages Solution** database in the **Solutions** folder.

Exercise 22

A sample solution for this exercise can be found in the **Commercial Solution** database in the **Solutions** folder.

Exercise 23

Step 10 **2** people.

Step 11 **24** days

Step 12 **Fresco** and **Green**

Step 16 **19** pages

A sample solution for this exercise can be found in the **Time Solution** database in the **Solutions** folder.

Exercise 24

Step 1 Because one **Computer** record may have many associated **Repair** records.

Step 2 "No unique index found for the referenced field of the primary table".

Step 4 One-to-Many.

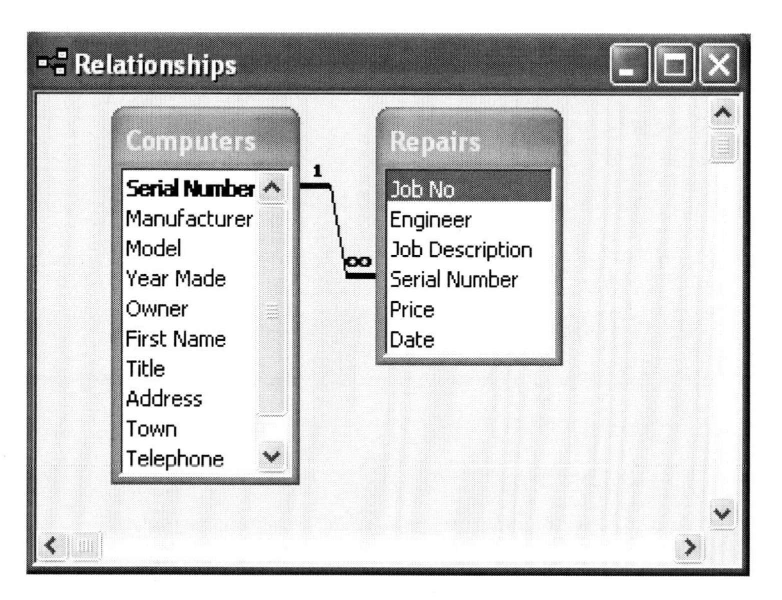

Step 6 Input mask **\0000\-0000000**

Step 10

```
SELECT TOP 5 Computers.Title, Computers.[First Name], Computers.Owner, Repairs.[Job Description], Repairs.Price, Repairs.Date
FROM Computers INNER JOIN Repairs ON Computers.[Serial Number] = Repairs.[Serial Number]
ORDER BY Repairs.Price DESC;
```

Step 13 **£469**

A sample solution for this exercise can be found in the **Repairs Solution** database in the **Solutions** folder.

Exercise 25

Step 4 **Manufacturing Unit** and **Store Unit**.

Step 7 **Offers2** contains the revised value, because it is a linked table.

Step 8 **>L00**

Step 9 Properties **M015** and **P007**

Step 11 **12** records.

Step 13 **28** records (premises with no offers are not included).

A sample solution for this exercise can be found in the **Agents Solution** database in the **Solutions** folder.

Exercise 26

Step 3 **195** records

Step 7 **8** records

Step 8 **15** records. Some projects will not have claims against them and so will not be included

Step 10 Highest Average Claim – **Project X**

Highest Number of Claims – **Southtown City Council**

Lowest Total Value of Claims – **Fresco Stock System**

A sample solution for this exercise can be found in the **Expenses Solution** database in the **Solutions** folder.

Exercise 27

Step 4 A **Junction** table is required to go between the two main tables. In this example the junction table is **Registration**.

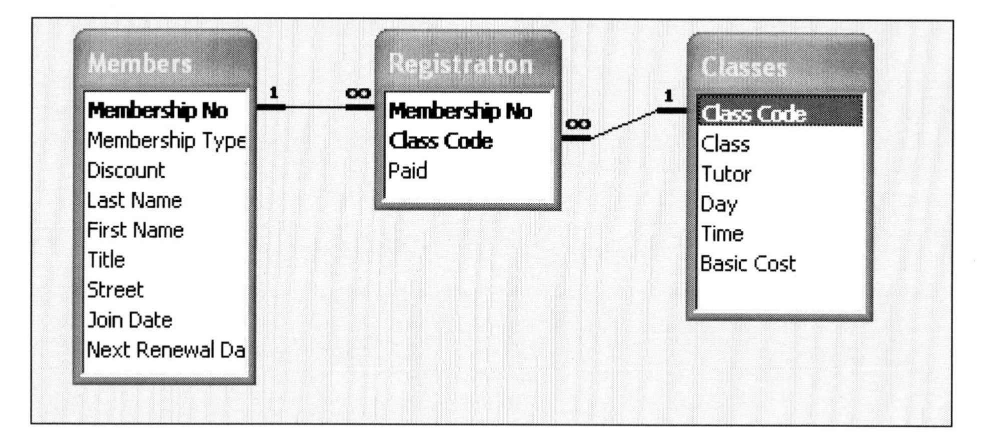

Step 5 **18** records selected.

Step 7 Classes **B3** and **G3** have no members enrolled.

Step 8 **3** records added.

A sample solution for this exercise can be found in the **Sports Solution** database in the **Solutions** folder.

Exercise 28

Step 2 **a)** There is a one-to-many relationship from **Mountains** to **Routes**.

Step 3 Different colour font, underlined, and cursor changes to a hand when over text.

Step 5 **2** records.

Step 6 **Is Null**.

Not Null would display only records with **Grades**.

Step 9 Lakeland Fells is an **Unbound** control. The control is not attached to any particular field from the database.

Route is a **Bound** control. The control is attached to the **Route** field from the **Routes** table.

Step 15 **4179** metres cumulative total after month 3.

A sample solution for this exercise can be found in the **Fells Solution** database in the **Solutions** folder.

Notes